BRAIN POWER

Quiz Book

This edition published in 2020 by Arcturus Publishing Limited
26/27 Bickels Yard, 151–153 Bermondsey Street,
London SE1 3HA

Author: Lisa Regan
Illustrator: Sr. Sanchez
Editor: Donna Gregory
Designer: Everitt Editorial
Author: Ivy Finnegan

CH007389NT
Supplier 10, Date 0620, Print run 10135

Printed in the UK

Contents

CHAPTER 1
General knowledge

1 What did the dinosaur Triceratops eat?

   a Fish   c Smaller dinosaurs
   b Plants   d Insects

2 Which famous London building is home to the
   Crown Jewels?

   a The Tower of London c Tower Bridge
   b Buckingham Palace   d City Hall

3 How should you play music if it says "adagio"
   on it?

   a Very quickly   c With your fingers
   b Slowly and at ease   d Silently

4 Cartography is the study and making of what?

   a Drawings   **c** Maps

   b Weapons   **d** Wagons

5 What is the main ingredient of the Swiss dish called rösti?

   a Corn   **c** Potatoes

   b Rice   **d** Roast meat

6 Which of these instruments does not have a piece called a bridge?

   a Guitar   **c** Flute

   b Lute   **d** Violin

7 What is the name of famous fictional detective Sherlock Holmes' faithful assistant?

   a Lucy the cat   **c** Dr. Crick

   b Dr. Watson   **d** Moriarty

8 What name is given to the trench filled with water that surrounds a castle?

a Moat
b Motte
c Lute
d Draw

9 What does RT mean on Twitter?

a Really talkative
b Retweet
c Ringtone
d Right

10 Which US President is the teddy bear named after?

a Harry S. Truman
b Theodore Roosevelt
c William Howard Taft
d Thomas Jefferson

11 Which prehistoric period was the earliest?

a Jurassic
b Permian
c Triassic
d Cretaceous

12 What is the name of Ron Weasley's pet rat in the Harry Potter books?

a Scamper

b Snitch

c Snape

d Scabbers

13 Which of these is the lowest type of female singing voice?

a Contralto

b Soprano

c Alto

d Tenor

14 What does a garrulous person do a lot of?

a Talking

b Sleeping

c Laughing

d Showing off

15 In which year was the Apple iPhone first released?

a 2003

b 2005

c 2007

d 2008

16 What is the name for a period of ten years?

17 What are aqueducts built to carry?

18 What O means a material that can't be seen through?

19 Which country's leaders have included Yeltsin and Medvedev?

20 How many triangular sides does an Egyptian pyramid have?

21 What nationality was the composer Mozart?

22 Which of Disney's seven dwarfs has no beard?

23 What fruit do sultanas and raisins come from?

24 What is the name of the traditional skirt worn by men in Scotland?

25 What replaced the peseta in Spain and the franc in France?

26 What kind of creature is Winnie-the-Pooh's friend Eeyore?

27 What number is represented by V in Roman numerals?

28 How would you say "thank you" in French?

29 What's the name of a person who designs buildings?

30 What is 0.75 as the lowest possible fraction?

31 What kind of transport can you catch at the Gare du Nord in Paris?

32 What letter is between A and D on a computer keyboard?

33 In *The Jungle Book*, what kind of creature is Kaa?

34 What is the French name for a long, thin loaf of bread?

35 Which C is an empty tomb or monument dedicated to a particular person or group?

36 Which legendary king had knights that met at a round table?

37 What did the suffragettes fight to get for women?

38 Which nanny could fly with the help of her umbrella?

39 What are you wearing if you are in your birthday suit?

40 Which baby animal was the star of *Babe*?

41 How many surfaces does a cube have?

42 What does YOLO stand for?

43 What G was an armed person who fought to entertain the ancient Romans?

44 Which item of clothing are you told to pull up if you need to do better at something?

45 What event are you at if you are watching a nuptial ceremony?

46 Which queen was the ruler of Britain at the start of the twentieth century?

47 How many musical notes are there in an octave?

48 Bramley and Granny Smith are what type of fruit?

49 What is a kiln used for?

50 What kind of creature is the ticking enemy of Captain Hook?

51 What is a mural painted on?

52 What grows in a paddy field?

53 Which ship sank in 1912 after hitting an iceberg?

54 What name is given to the large words above a newspaper story?

55 What name is given to the apartment at the top of a building?

56 A prune is a dried version of which fruit?

57 What S is a shadow outline filled with black?

58 Ivan the Terrible and Catherine the Great were leaders of which country?

59 What is the name for a non-magical person in the Harry Potter books?

60 What language was spoken in Ancient Rome?

61 What is Dorothy's dog called in the *Wizard of Oz*?

62 Who cut off the tails of the Three Blind Mice?

63 What nationality were the composers Verdi and Vivaldi?

64 Which food has varieties called romaine, cos, and iceberg?

65 What C is an ornamental candlestick?

66 The Pilgrim Fathers sailed from England to Massachusetts on which boat?

67 The year 1999 was in which century?

68 Which part of the body does a chiropodist look after?

69 Which cartoon duck has nephews called Huey, Dewey, and Louie?

70 Which green-fleshed fruit is used to make guacamole?

71 Which British Prime Minister's first names were Winston Spencer?

72 What number is represented by C in Roman numerals?

73 What G was a machine used in the French Revolution to chop off people's heads?

74 What shade do you get if you mix together blue and yellow?

75 How many days are there in a leap year?

76 What letter is between B and M on a computer keyboard?

77 Which language is commonly used for musical terms?

78 In which year did World War I start?

79 In which country will you find Gatwick Airport?

80 Who wrote *The Jungle Book*?

81 Which type of pizza is folded over to conceal the fillings?

82 How many years are there in a century?

83 What is notable about a group of a cappella singers?

84 What A is a book written by a person, about themselves?

85 What staple food is made from durum wheat?

86 How many strings does a violin have?

87 If someone says "DM me" what does it mean?

88 Which is the shortest month of the year?

89 What pulled a Roman chariot along the road?

90 Which sweet food is added to fruit and cream to make pavlova?

91 How many sides does a hexagon have?

92 What are there 168 of in a week?

93 Granny, reef, and slip are all kinds of what?

94 What is the plural of "elf"?

95 What is the first name of the Italian designer Armani?

96 What A is a single word for loss of memory?

97 What number is represented by D in Roman numerals?

98 Which country tried to invade England with a fleet of ships called the Armada?

99 In *The Jungle Book*, what kind of animal is Baloo?

100 What nationality were the composers Bach and Beethoven?

101 What does the social media abbreviation AFAIK stand for?

102 What is the name of Harry Potter's cousin with whom he has to live?

103 On which London street does the British Prime Minister live?

104 What C was the name adopted by Roman Emperors?

105 Which language is commonly used for ballet terms?

106 In which wood does Winnie-the-Pooh live?

✎

107 What kind of transport can you catch at JFK in New York?

✎

108 For what are Sir Edmund Hillary and Tenzing Norgay most famous?

✎

109 What does FOMO stand for?

✎

110 What part of a ship is its prow?

✎

111 What is the capital city of India?

✎

112 What town is associated with the Pied Piper?

113 What shade do you get if you mix together red and yellow?

114 What letter is between Y and I on a computer keyboard?

115 Who was the Roman god of the sea?

116 How many seconds are there in a minute and a half?

117 What B describes a person who speaks two languages fluently?

118 What number is represented by L in Roman numerals?

119 Beefsteak is a variety of tomato. True or false?

120 Roads built by the Romans were usually straight. True or false?

121 King Henry VIII of England had five wives. True or false?

122 Bill Clinton was the President of the US before Barack Obama. True or false?

123 The fattest string on a guitar makes the highest notes. True or false?

124 Changi Airport is found in Singapore. True or false?

125 The Stone Age happened before the Bronze Age. True or false?

126 During the Prohibition Period in America, it was illegal to buy tea. True or false?

127 In *The Jungle Book*, Hathi is a monkey. True or false?

128 Charles Darwin did much of his exploring on a ship called *HMS Labrador*. True or false?

129 The *Mona Lisa* was painted in the 1500s by Leonardo di Caprio. True or false?

130 The ancient rulers of India and Iran were called Shah. True or false?

CHAPTER 2
Animals and Nature

1 Which of these does not live in Africa?

  a Giraffe   **c** Chimpanzee

  b Jaguar   **d** Cheetah

2 Where is a great white shark's dorsal fin?

  a Its tail   **c** Its back

  b In front of the tail   **d** By its gills

3 Which wild animal lives in a warren?

  a Fox   **c** Rabbit

  b Squirrel   **d** Owl

4   In which kind of habitat does a fennec fox live?

   a Rain forest   **c** Woodland
   b Desert   **d** Mountains

5   Which of these is not a reptile?

   a Tortoise   **c** Iguana
   b Python   **d** Armadillo

6   What is a whale doing when it breaches?

   a Breathing   **c** Diving
   b Jumping   **d** Breeding

7   What is a large group of bees called?

   a A swarm   **c** A fuzz
   b A buzz   **d** A cluster

8 What are the male parts of a flower called?

    a Sepals   **c** Stamens

    b Petals   **d** Pistils

9 What is the baobab, found in Africa?

    a Cactus   **c** Tree

    b Monkey   **d** Snake

10 Which of these can sleep standing up?

    a Sheep   **c** Horse

    b Goat   **d** Hedgehog

11 Where are a grasshopper's ears located?

    a Body   **c** Head

    b Feet   **d** Tongue

12 Which is the longest species of snake?

   a Boa constrictor   **c** Rattlesnake

   b Reticulated python   **d** Corn snake

13 What does a vertebrate have that an invertebrate does not?

   a Eyes   **c** Spine

   b Skeleton   **d** Friends

14 Which of these is best known for its song?

   a Humpback whale   **c** Warthog

   b Penguin   **d** Meerkat

15 Pug, poodle, and collie are types of what?

   a Dog   **c** Ape

   b Horse   **d** Tortoise

16 What are female elephants called?

17 How many legs does a spider have?

18 Which relative of seals has huge tusks?

19 What O is a word for a collection of fruit trees?

20 What venomous snake has a hood?

21 What is a group of birds called?

22 In which kind of habitat does a giraffe live?

23 Which farmed bird has the same name as a country?

24 What do kangaroos eat?

25 What type of creature is a gila monster?

26 Which pet is nicknamed Man's Best Friend?

27 What kind of creature can be spectacled, grizzly, or Kodiak?

28 Where does a chimpanzee sleep?

29 What do people build for bees to live in?

30 What is the fastest land animal in the world?

31 A group of lions is known as what?

32 How many pairs of wings does a bee have?

33 What C is a small striped ground squirrel?

34 What is a baby swan known as?

35 What name is given to a plant that loses its leaves each year?

36 What are baby goats called?

37 Which relative of the weasel has webbed feet and eats fish?

38 Lemurs are a native animal of which island?

39 Which pouched animal pretends to be dead to protect itself?

40 From which kind of tree do we get acorns?

41 Why does a snake shed its skin?

42 Which blobby creature makes up a large part of the leatherback turtle's diet?

43 Which is the biggest type of penguin?

44 What general name is given to an animal that sits at the top of the food chain?

45 Which type of bird can fly backward and sideways?

46 Do snakes have ears?

47 Which of these is not a mammal? Tenrec, okapi, hyrax, civet, loris, lory.

48 What process do most plants use to make food from sunlight?

49 What is the name for a female fox?

50 In which kind of habitat does a manatee live?

51 Which yellow bird has the same name as a group of holiday islands in the Atlantic?

52 How many years does a perennial plant live for— one, two, or several?

53 Springer, King Charles, and Cocker are breeds of which dog?

54 What pattern does an okapi have on its bottom?

55 Which rain forest is the largest in the world?

56 Which is bigger, a fully grown elephant or hippo?

57 Which of these is not a fish? Gurnard, quail, wrasse, tarpon, gourami, skate.

58 Which part of a plant is underground and stops the plant falling over?

59 What is a baby kangaroo known as?

60 Why does a rattlesnake make a rattling noise?

61 On which continent are New World monkeys found?

62 Which is bigger, a tiger or a polar bear?

63 Which crab doesn't grow a shell of its own, but borrows discarded ones?

64 What kind of creature is a black widow?

65 What is a mermaid's purse?

66 How does a dandelion spread its seeds?

67 What do tadpoles turn into?

68 Do zebras live alone or in a herd?

69 What name is given to a fox's tail? (Hint: you could paint with it.)

70 Is a giraffe's tongue reddish-pink, greenish-blue, or purplish-black?

71 What type of scientist studies plant life?

72 What kind of animal is a filly?

73 What is the name for the flowers found on fruit trees?

74 Which bird is a symbol of peace?

75 What breed of dog is commonly used to pull a sledge?

76 What type of bear lives the farthest north?

77 Which continent do gorillas come from?

78 When is a diurnal creature most active?

79 Which mammal helped to spread the Black Death in the 1300s?

80 What shape does a sun bear have on its chest?

81 Which part of a whale is known as its flukes?

CHAPTER 2

82 Which animal has horns known as ossicones on its head?

83 What name is given to a plant that stores its seeds in cones?

84 Which is bigger, a horse or a pony?

85 Which D is an Australian relative of the wolf?

86 What do walruses eat?

87 Which of these is not a bird? Lory, rhea, booby, skua, genet, hoopoe.

88 Which moves more slowly, a snail or a sloth?

40

89 Which continent do llamas and alpacas come from?

90 What do all baby mammals feed on at first?

91 What type of creatures gather in a shoal?

92 Which part of the hand is also the name for a type of tree?

93 What is a name for a male deer?

94 In which kind of habitat does a meerkat live?

95 Do dolphins have gills for breathing?

96 Which tree has a name that suggests it is crying?

97 Which tree-dweller lives almost entirely on a diet of eucalyptus leaves?

98 What kind of creature is a thorny devil?

99 What does a three-banded armadillo do when it is frightened?

100 How many toes does a rhinoceros foot have?

101 How does a crocodile carry its young?

102 What is the largest type of ape?

103 A wallaby is a small type of what?

104 Are baboons and macaques apes or monkeys?

105 What is a hunting group of wolves known as?

106 Are butterflies insects or arachnids?

107 What are male elephants called?

108 How many legs does a scorpion have?

109 Which bird lays its eggs in other birds' nests?

110 How many leaves does a shamrock have?

111 Which F is a pink bird with long legs?

112 What is a social group of dolphins known as?

113 On which continent do emus live in the wild?

114 Which plant makes up nearly all of a giant panda's diet?

115 What is the largest living fish?

116 What animal carries its food store on its back as part of its body?

117 What is the name of the phobia that involves an abnormal fear of spiders?

118 Giraffes live in the wild on which continent?

119 How many legs does a lobster have?

120 What C is the largest living reptile?

121 Which Australian animal has poisonous spikes on the male's back legs?

122 Perch and skate are what kind of creatures?

123 What are the openings called on the side of a shark, used for breathing?

124 The dromedary camel has two humps. True or false?

125 A dik-dik is an African bird. True or false?

126 An aardvark and an aardwolf are both insect-eating animals. True or false?

127 Crocodiles release heat through their mouth as they can't sweat. True or false?

128 All apes have tails. True or false?

129 The dodo and the quagga are both types of extinct creature. True or false?

130 A manta ray is a type of insect. True or false?

131 A rhea can fly. True or false?

132 Dolphins and whales are fish. True or false?

133 The gavial is a fish-eating crocodile from India. True or false?

134 A skink is a type of lizard. True or false?

135 The pinna is part of a sea lion's flipper. True or false?

136 The hoatzin bird has chicks that use claws on their wings to climb trees. True or false?

137 A chameleon is a reptile. True or false?

CHAPTER 3
Sports and Pastimes

1 In a motorsport race, what flag is waved to show the drivers the race has been stopped?

a A red flag

b An orange flag

c A black and white flag

d A triangular flag

2 How does a swimmer register that they have finished their race?

a By waving

b By climbing out

c By touching the wall

d By standing up

3 Which boy's name is also the name of the target ball in bowls?

a Jack

b Tim

c Bob

d Paul

4 The martial art karate originates from which country?

   a China   **c** Turkey

   b Japan   **d** Russia

5 How many events are there in a heptathlon?

   a Five   **c** Ten

   b Seven   **d** Twelve

6 Which of these is not found in the woodwind section of an orchestra?

   a Clarinet   **c** Tuba

   b Oboe   **d** Flute

7 Which of these is a term in golf?

   a Falcon   **c** Parrot

   b Eagle   **d** Canary

8 What's the real name of the Australian swimmer who was nicknamed "the Thorpedo"?

  a Dana Thorpe   **c** Thoria Miler
  b Thor Magnusson   **d** Ian Thorpe

9 The martial art capoeira originates from which country?

  a China   **c** Russia
  b Brazil   **d** Peru

10 What is the name of the peg that a golfer places the ball on before taking their first shot?

  a Dee   **c** Tee
  b Pee   **d** Queue

11 What are the games called in a snooker match?

  a Legs   **c** Frames
  b Squares   **d** Bouts

12 A red polka dot jersey is awarded in cycling to the king of the what?

- **a** Saddle
- **b** Sprints
- **c** Mountains
- **d** Wheelies

13 What is the target score in a game of darts?

- **a** 299
- **b** 351
- **c** 442
- **d** 501

14 Which sport is regulated by the Queensberry Rules?

- **a** Baseball
- **b** Basketball
- **c** Boxing
- **d** Bowling

15 Which of these is the last event in a decathlon?

- **a** Triple jump
- **b** Discus
- **c** 1500m
- **d** Marathon

16 In which sport could you watch butterfly and freestyle?

17 What is the name of the layered skirt worn by female ballet dancers?

18 How many players are there on a baseball team?

19 Which C is a famous French dance involving high kicks and splits?

20 A judoka participates in what sport?

21 Which standard domino has the most spots?

22 Which race is longer, 1500m or 1 mile?

23 Which game is played on a lawn with mallets and hoops?

24 Which game is played on horseback using a mallet?

25 In which board game do you receive money for passing the "Go" space?

26 What name is given to a bike with one wheel?

27 What is the name of the stick that has to be passed on in a relay race?

28 What material do you need for the hobby of origami?

29 Which sport is described as "the art of attacking or defending with a sword"?

30 How many wheels are there on a regular skateboard?

31 What nationality was the composer Tchaikovsky?

32 How many points has a tennis player scored if their score is "love"?

33 How many black and white squares are there on a chess board?

34 What position did you finish in a race if you win a Bronze medal?

35 Which ball scores the most points if you pot it in snooker?

36 How many rings are on the flag of the Olympic Games?

37 Downhill racing, cross-country, and jumping are all winter sports that need which equipment?

38 Which animal competes at the Olympic Games?

39 How long does each round last in a boxing match?

40 What is a bunker on a golf course filled with?

41 How many players are there on a cricket team?

42 In swimming, what kind of race is a medley?

43 How many feet positions are there in modern classical ballet?

44 What instrument does the leader of an orchestra play?

45 In baseball, what is a double play?

46 In cricket, which country competes for the Ashes against England?

47 How many performers are there in a duet?

48 In combat sports, what does MMA stand for?

49 With what do games of American football, soccer and rugby all start?

50 Where did the 2016 Summer Olympic Games take place?

51 What type of animal would you see in a dressage event?

52 For which sport is Steffi Graf famous?

53 What is the middle of a dartboard called?

54 How often do the summer Olympic Games take place?

✗

55 Which pastime with a Japanese name means "empty orchestra" in English?

✗

56 In baseball, how many strikes are called by the umpire before the batter is out?

✗

57 When white moves first in a game of chess, which piece could be moved instead of a pawn?

✗

58 In what game is the score sometimes "deuce"?

✗

59 A piccolo is a small version of which woodwind instrument?

60 How many players are there on a wheelchair basketball team?

61 How many balls are used in a game of Quidditch?

62 What does it mean in golf when a hole is "par 4"?

63 What is the name of the white ball in snooker?

64 Which sport puts the fastest qualifier in pole position?

65 How many players are there on a netball team?

66 What is it called when a player scores three goals in one game?

67 What does a dancer do during a pirouette?

68 What is the edge of the field called in cricket?

69 What do you call a winning serve in tennis?

70 What is another name for angling?

71 What is England's most famous tennis tournament?

72 In which sport can you dribble but not travel?

73 How many legs does a tripod have?

74 How many pockets are there on a snooker table?

75 What sport would you play if you competed for the Stanley Cup?

76 For which sport was Muhammad Ali famous?

77 In which sport might you play goal keeper, goal attack, or goal shooter?

78 What shape of ball is used in Australian rules football?

79 Which country's rugby union team is known as the All Blacks?

80 Tennis can be played on concrete, clay, and which other surface?

81 In which pastime might you perform a battement or a chassé?

82 How many innings does a baseball game normally last?

83 For which sport was Pele famous?

84 How many gymnastics events do men compete in at the Olympic Games?

85 In which sport, first introduced in Ancient Greece, might you perform a jab or an uppercut?

86 What are the names of the suits in a standard deck of playing cards?

87 How many runners are in a relay race team?

88 Which sport scores fours and sixes in an innings?

89 If the Tour de France is in France, where does the Giro take place?

90 In which sport might the commentator announce, "Her stone has finished right on the button"?

91 Which sport is also known as Association football?

92 In a grand slam tennis match, how many sets does a male player have to win to beat his opponent?

93 Which wind instrument is associated with Scotland?

94 In combat sports, what does KO stand for?

95 What does a ballet dancer do during a plié?

96 In a motorsport race, what does a red and yellow striped flag mean?

97 How do you make a musical sound with maracas?

98 For which sport was Babe Ruth famous?

99 How many players are on a tennis court in a game of doubles?

100 The FIFA World Cup is a competition for which sport?

101 What sport is being played if you are watching the Six Nations Championship?

102 How many tennis tournaments make up the Grand Slam?

103 Which sport has a "charity stripe" or foul line?

104 For which sport was Martina Navratilova famous?

105 Tango, foxtrot, and samba are all types of what?

106 What position do you play in soccer if you are nominated for the Golden Glove award?

107 In which sport might you get a fastball, curveball or a knuckleball?

108 Which sport has free kicks and scrimmage kicks?

109 How many events are there in a decathlon?

110 How many holes are played in a round of golf?

111 In which sport is the main group known as the peloton?

112 In basketball, where do you go if you are fouled while shooting?

113 How many playing sessions are there in a netball match?

114 For which sport was Shaquille O'Neal famous?

115 In golf, what does a caddie do?

116 How many players take part in a darts match?

117 How does a game of Quidditch end?

118 A boxing ring is round. True or false?

119 In a swimming medley relay, breaststroke is always done first. True or false?

120 The Azzurri is the nickname for many of the sports teams from India. True or false?

121 In a motorsport race, a black flag means that the driver has been disqualified. True or false?

122 BMX racing is an Olympic sport. True or false?

123 In Major League Baseball, the visiting team always bats first. True or false?

124 Bossaball is played on an inflatable court with trampolines on each side of the net. True or false?

125 The word "origami" comes from the Japanese for "cutting" and "paper." True or false?

126 There is a sport known as chessboxing that combines chess and boxing. True or false?

127 Boxing is also known by the name pugilism. True or false?

128 In Spain, soccer is known as calcio. True or false?

129 An ice hockey match begins with a face off. True or false?

CHAPTER 4
Science and technology

1 Which disease is commonly transmitted by mosquitoes?

  a Influenza   **c** Pneumonia

  b Asthma   **d** Malaria

2 What does a paleontologist study?

  a Rocks   **c** Fossils

  b Insects   **d** Planets

3 Which of these planets does not have rings?

  a Saturn   **c** Neptune

  b Venus   **d** Uranus

4 What type of lens is a magnifying glass?

  a Contract   **c** Convex

  b Concave   **d** Conform

5 What is the name for a strong fear of open places?

  a Aquaphobia   **c** Claustrophobia

  b Agoraphobia   **d** Panophobia

6 What was the first name of scientist Faraday, known for his work on electricity?

  a William   **c** Pierre

  b Tristan   **d** Michael

7 What type of animal was Ham, sent into space in 1961 by the USA?

  a Chimpanzee   **c** Pig

  b Hamster   **d** Dog

8 What does an ammeter measure?

   a Electrical resistance   **c** Electric force

   b Electric current   **d** Electric fence

9 Which part of the body is most often affected by bronchitis?

   a Lungs   **c** Liver

   b Heart   **d** Brain

10 Who was the first woman in space?

   a Maria Sharapova   **c** Mae Jemison

   b Valentina Tereshkova   **d** Sally Ride

11 What name is given to the movement of muscles to push food through the body?

   a Kinesis   **c** Osmosis

   b Peristalsis   **d** Hypnosis

12 What does a lepidopterist study?

   a Fossils   **c** Rocks
   b Rabbits   **d** Butterflies

13 Sputnik was the first example of what to be sent into space?

   a Monkey   **c** Satellite
   b Reusable rocket   **d** Spider

14 A long line of vertebrae are more commonly known as what?

   a The ribs   **c** The toes
   b The spine   **d** The teeth

15 Which scientist is well known for his laws of motion?

   a Isaac Newton   **c** Charles Darwin
   b Stephen Hawking   **d** Lewis Hamilton

16 In computing, what does AI stand for?

17 Which is bigger: Mars or Venus?

18 How many ribs does a human have?

19 What N is a word describing the feeling that you want to be sick?

20 Which chemical element is represented by the letter C?

21 What is the name of the opening in the middle of your eye?

22 Arachnophobia is a fear of what?

23 What is the wire inside an electric lightbulb called?

24 What C means dog-like?

25 Which disease affects the body's production of, or response to, insulin?

26 What is H_2O more commonly known as?

27 Where were the Apollo space missions intended to study?

28 If vision is related to sight, what is olfaction related to?

29 How many teeth does an adult human normally have (including their wisdom teeth)?

30 Which two garden minibeasts can be the names of computer problems?

31 Mars, Venus, and Earth are in which galaxy?

32 Plasma and platelets are found in which part of the body?

33 What does an ornithologist study: birds, snakes, or bees?

34 Which organ pumps blood around the body?

35 What was Einstein's first name?

36 Where is the largest bone in your body?

37 What does an entomologist study: birds, sharks or insects?

38 What is the middle of an atom called?

39 How many times does the Earth go around the Sun in one year?

40 If every member of a species dies, what is this known as?

41 Strong magnets are mostly made of which metal?

42 What gas do plants absorb from the atmosphere?

43 Which planet comes nearest to Earth in its orbit?

44 Which chemical element with the symbol Ne is often used to make red lights?

45 Which appears first in a storm: thunder or lightning?

46 Where is your cerebrum located?

47 Which is bigger: Saturn or Neptune?

48 What is the opposite of transparent: translucent or opaque?

49 What type of software are Norton and McAfee?

50 What force draws objects toward a planet?

51 Is iron found mostly in human bones, blood, or hair?

52 In computing, what does CPU stand for?

53 Which is higher: room temperature or body temperature?

54 Metals expand when heated and do what when cooled?

55 What everyday substance does a saline solution have in it?

56 What name is given to the chest bones that protect your organs?

57 What H is an animal that is best adapted to eating plants?

58 Which chemical element is represented by the letter O?

59 What does a botanist study?

60 Which planet has a large volcano called Olympus Mons?

61 What is the main gas in the air we breathe?

62 If vulpine means "fox-like," which animal does equine describe?

63 Which four planets are known as the rocky planets?

64 In which part of the body is the ulna?

65 What is the Russian name for an astronaut?

66 What do eyelashes protect us from?

67 What was the first name of Newton, famous for his laws of motion?

68 Which is the largest planet in the solar system?

69 What kind of plant do grapes grow on?

70 What does the "e" in email stand for?

71 How many chambers does a cow's stomach have?

72 In which part of the body are the quadriceps?

73 Which is bigger: Venus or Earth?

74 What F means cat-like?

75 How many lungs does a human have?

76 What shade are most emeralds?

77 What are four babies born at one time called?

78 What is the square root of 81?

79 What is the larynx also known as?

80 Which scientist is well known for his theory of relativity?

81 Which planet is the nearest to the Sun?

82 If vulpine means "fox-like," which animal does bovine describe?

83 In which part of the body is the septum?

84 Who do you visit for an eye test?

85 What are Saturn's rings mostly made of?

86 Which company did Steve Jobs and Steve Wozniak set up in 1976?

87 What is the name for a portable computer with a keyboard?

88 Which planet is known as the Red Planet?

89 What do we call a male bee or an unmanned aerial vehicle?

90 On what kind of sea-going vessel would you find a periscope?

91 Which is not an input device: a mouse, a touch screen, or headphones?

92 What luxurious fabric is made with the help of moth caterpillars?

93 In computing, what does FTP stand for?

94 What V is a person who travels and also a space probe that has explored the outer planets in the solar system?

95 What's the first element on the periodic table?

96 In computing, what does ROM stand for?

97 What moves between the Sun and the Earth during a solar eclipse?

98 Which part of the body has two ventricles?

99 Which company did Bill Gates and Paul Allen set up in 1975?

100 In nuclear fission, does the nucleus of an atom split into smaller parts, or join into bigger ones?

101 Which four planets are known as the gas giants?

102 What connects the middle of a bicycle wheel to its outer edge?

103 What name is given to moving to a warmer place for the winter?

104 How many bits in a byte?

105 Which planet in the solar system is the farthest from the Sun?

106 What is a thing for crossing a river and the control place on a ship?

107 In computing, what does the I of IP stand for?

108 Acids have a pH below 7. True or false?

109 An electron carries a positive charge. True or false?

110 Neptune orbits the Sun faster than Jupiter. True or false?

111 Batteries convert chemical energy to electrical energy. True or false?

112 Your chest is the main part affected if you have gastric flu. True or false?

113 The Sun is the only star in our solar system. True or false?

114 Gold is heavier than silver. True or false?

115 A long-sighted person has trouble seeing things that are far away. True or false?

116 A terabyte is bigger than a gigabyte. True or false?

117 Copernicus's theory of heliocentrism said that the planets orbit the Sun, not the Earth. True or false?

118 An apex predator has more enemies than other animals. True or false?

119 There are around 206 bones in the adult human body. True or false?

CHAPTER 5
People and Places

1 What kind of bridge is San Francisco's Golden Gate Bridge?

    a Cantilever   **c** Suspension

    b Trestle   **d** Rickety

2 Where are most Tyrannosaurus rex fossils found?

    a North America   **c** South America

    b China   **d** Australia

3 What do you do with an Indian tandoor?

    a Wash   **c** Play tunes

    b Cook   **d** Paint

4 How many countries are there in South America?

   a 12   **c** 19

   b 15   **d** 23

5 Which of these is a mountain in South Africa?

   a Bed Mountain   **c** Sofa Mountain

   b Desk Mountain   **d** Table Mountain

6 Lagos, one of the fastest-growing cities in the world, is in which country?

   a India   **c** Nigeria

   b China   **d** Cameroon

7 Which one of these is a fossil fuel?

   a Wind   **c** Iron

   b Natural gas   **d** Bones

8 Where is couscous most commonly eaten?

  a Africa   **c** Asia

  b Australia   **d** South America

9 In which year did the Eiffel Tower open?

  a 1799   **c** 1929

  b 1889   **d** 1949

10 What does a seismologist study?

  a Rocks   **c** Earthquakes

  b Fish   **d** Rivers

11 Which is the largest Scandinavian country?

  a Finland   **c** Norway

  b Sweden   **d** Denmark

12 Provincial describes all parts of a country except for what?

  a The capital   **c** The cities

  b The coast   **d** The mountains

13 What creature is on the middle white stripe of Egypt's flag?

  a An eagle   **c** A scorpion

  b A snake   **d** A dove

14 Which of these is not part of France's motto?

  a Liberty   **c** Equality

  b Community   **d** Fraternity

15 Which of these is an underground layer of rock with water in it?

  a Aqueduct   **c** Potifer

  b Aquifer   **d** Pothole

16 What is the capital city of Spain?

17 Which ocean can you see from California?

18 What B is a severe snow storm?

19 Which country is the second largest country in the world by area?

20 In which continent is Belarus?

21 What C always points north and is used for navigating?

22 What are the two longest rivers in the world?

PEOPLE AND PLACES

23 What is measured on the Richter scale?

24 On which continent is Denali (Mount McKinley)?

25 Shanghai and Beijing are the two largest cities in which country?

26 Which is the tallest building in New York?

27 On which continent is the Sahara Desert?

28 The rand is the official currency of which country?

29 Which country's only border is with Spain?

30 Which word beginning with E means the mouth of a river?

31 The Potomac River flows through which capital city?

32 Coal, oil, and natural gas are the three main types of what?

33 On which continent is the Kalahari Desert?

34 What name is given to a huge, often moving, mound of sand?

35 What name is given to the big wheel ride on the banks of London's River Thames?

36 Which Italian city has a famous leaning tower?

37 Which has more people living in it, Chicago or Los Angeles?

38 What is the capital city of Germany?

39 The ruble is the official currency of which enormous country?

40 Mumbai, Delhi, and Bangalore are three of the largest cities in which country?

41 Which is bigger, Canada or the US?

42 Which US state is in the Pacific Ocean?

43 Which currency is used in Italy, Spain, and France?

44 In which country is a kimono traditionally worn?

45 Which country experiences the most tornadoes?

46 What are the famous boats of Venice called?

47 What is a country's official song called?

48 How many states are there in Australia: 4, 6, or 8?

49 A Samurai is a Japanese what?

50 What treat is made from the cocoa bean?

51 What instrument is used to measure temperature?

52 Who are the native people of New Zealand?

53 Which London cathedral has a dome?

54 Where does a Scotsman wear a Tam o'shanter?

55 What is a mariner?

56 A tropical cyclone over the Atlantic Ocean is known as what?

57 Which river flows through Egypt's capital, Cairo?

58 What are the official currencies of India, Pakistan, and Sri Lanka all called?

59 On which continent is the Great Sandy Desert?

60 Which city are you in if you are at the top of the Empire State Building?

61 On which continent is the Atacama Desert?

62 Which is the smallest of the oceans?

63 Which European country is shaped like a boot?

64 By what name is the Netherlands also known?

65 What name is given to a home made of snow?

66 Manhattan is part of which large city?

67 Which canal links the Atlantic Ocean with the Pacific Ocean?

68 Which is bigger: Spain or France?

69 In which continent is Venezuela?

70 Which capital city is also the name of a boot?

71 What cave formation is formed by minerals dripping from the ceiling?

72 Which sea would you swim in if you were staying on Spain's Costa del Sol?

73 What is the name for hot, molten rock when it pours from a volcano?

74 The US has coastlines on which two large oceans?

75 In which continent is Vietnam?

76 What kind of transport can you catch at the Hauptbahnhof in Berlin?

77 What F is a break in the Earth at the boundary of two plates?

78 Where is the "Land of the Rising Sun"?

79 Cumulus, cirrus, and stratus are types of what?

80 Which city's nickname is "The Big Apple"?

81 Parmesan cheese comes from which country?

82 What does a meteorologist study? (Clue: It isn't meteors!)

83 What type of boat carries cars and people across rivers or seas?

84 What is the official language of Austria?

85 On which continent is Mount Kilimanjaro?

86 What M is a kind of rock formed by heating and squashing?

87 What is the capital city of Italy?

88 Which US state is to the west of Canada?

89 Which country's flag is a red square with a white cross?

90 Trying to predict the weather is known as weather … what?

91 Moussaka is a national dish of which country?

92 What animal's body does the Great Sphinx of Giza have?

93 In which continent is Ecuador?

94 What is the name of the active volcano found in Sicily?

95 What is a sombrero?

96 Which is the world's smallest continent?

97 What is the official currency of Mexico, Chile, and Argentina?

98 What is the largest state of the US?

99 What A is a rapid movement downhill of large amounts of snow?

100 What kind of transport can you catch at Schiphol in the Netherlands?

101 What kind of sauce is served on the Canadian dish poutine?

102 In which American city is the Statue of Liberty situated?

103 Which of the Seven Wonders of the World is in Egypt?

104 What name was given to the ancient rulers of China and Japan?

105 What F is prehistoric remains that have been preserved in rock?

106 If you order crêpes in France, what food will you receive?

107 What is the capital city of Japan?

108 On which continent are the Himalayan mountains?

109 What is the name of the river that runs through the Grand Canyon?

110 Three US states are not joined to the others. True or false?

111 The South Pole is warmer than the North Pole. True or false?

112 The Dead Sea is roughly nine times saltier than the Atlantic Ocean. True or false?

113 Goulash is a paprika-based stew, common in Hungary. True or false?

114 Fossils of sea creatures are more common than fossils of land animals. True or false?

115 The Statue of Liberty was given to the US as a gift from Canada. True or false?

116 The surface area of North America's Great Lakes is roughly the same size as the UK. True or false?

117 Sedimentary rocks are formed by the cooling of volcanic lava. True or false?

118 There are four Great Lakes in North America. True or false?

119 Over two-thirds of the Earth's surface is water. True or false?

120 Stalagmites hang from the ceiling of caves. True or false?

121 Diamond is the hardest mineral in the world. True or false?

Answers

How many questions did you get right? Check here for all of the answers!

Answers

CHAPTER 1

pages 4–5

1 Plants
2 The Tower of London
3 Slowly and at ease
4 Maps
5 Potatoes
6 Flute
7 Dr. Watson

pages 6–7

8 Moat
9 Retweet
10 Theodore Roosevelt
11 Permian
12 Scabbers
13 Contralto
14 Talking
15 2007

pages 8–9

16 Decade
17 Water

18 Opaque
19 Russia
20 Four
21 Austrian
22 Dopey
23 Grapes
24 Kilt
25 The Euro
26 A donkey
27 5
28 Merci

pages 10–11

29 Architect
30 Three-quarters
31 Train
32 S
33 A snake
34 Baguette
35 Cenotaph
36 King Arthur
37 A vote at elections
38 Mary Poppins
39 Nothing!
40 A piglet

Answers

pages 12–13

41 Six

42 You only live once

43 Gladiator

44 Your socks

45 A wedding

46 Queen Victoria

47 Eight

48 Apple

49 Baking pottery or bricks to make them hard

50 A crocodile

51 A wall

52 Rice

53 The *Titanic*

pages 14–15

54 The headline

55 Penthouse

56 Plum

57 Silhouette

58 Russia

59 Muggle

60 Latin

61 Toto

62 The farmer's wife

63 Italian

64 Lettuce

65 Candelabra

66 The *Mayflower*

pages 16–17

67 Twentieth

68 The feet

69 Donald Duck

70 Avocado

71 Churchill

72 100

73 Guillotine

74 Green

75 366

76 N

77 Italian

78 1914

pages 18–19

79 UK (or England)

80 Rudyard Kipling

81 Calzone

82 100

83 They are singing

Answers

without a musical accompaniment

84 Autobiography

85 Pasta

86 Four

87 Send them a Direct Message

88 February

89 Horses

90 Meringue

91 6

92 Hours

pages 20–21

93 Knots

94 Elves

95 Giorgio

96 Amnesia

97 500

98 Spain

99 A bear

100 German

101 As far as I know

102 Dudley Dursley

103 Downing Street

104 Caesar

105 French

pages 22–23

106 Hundred Acre Wood

107 Plane

108 Being the first climbers to reach the summit of Mount Everest

109 Fear of missing out

110 The front

111 New Delhi

112 Hamelin

113 Orange

114 U

115 Neptune

116 90

117 Bilingual

118 50

pages 24–25

119 T

120 T

121 F (He had six wives.)

Answers

122 F (It was George W. Bush.)

123 F (The thinnest string makes the highest notes.)

124 T

125 T

126 F (It was illegal to buy alcoholic drinks.)

127 F (Hathi is an elephant.)

128 F (It was called *HMS Beagle*.)

129 F (It was painted by Leonardo da Vinci.)

130 T

Answers

CHAPTER 2

pages 26-27

1 Jaguar
2 Its back
3 Rabbit
4 Desert
5 Armadillo
6 Jumping
7 A swarm

pages 28-29

8 Stamens
9 Tree
10 Horse
11 Body
12 Reticulated python
13 Spine
14 Humpback whale
15 Dog

pages 30-31

16 Cows
17 Eight
18 Walrus
19 Orchard

20 Cobra
21 A flock
22 Grasslands or savanna
23 Turkey
24 Grass and leaves
25 A large lizard
26 A dog
27 Bear
28 In a nest in the trees
29 A hive

pages 32-33

30 Cheetah
31 A pride
32 Two
33 Chipmunk
34 Cygnet
35 Deciduous
36 Kids
37 Otter
38 Madagascar
39 Opossum
40 Oak
41 To allow it to grow
42 Jellyfish

Answers

pages 34–35

43 The emperor penguin

44 Apex predator

45 Hummingbird

46 No, they "hear" vibrations through their jawbone.

47 Lory (a parrot)

48 Photosynthesis

49 Vixen

50 Rivers, estuaries, and shallow ocean water

51 Canary

52 Several

53 Spaniel

54 Stripes

55 The Amazon

pages 36–37

56 An elephant

57 Quail

58 The roots

59 Joey

60 To warn off its enemies

61 South America

62 Polar bear

63 Hermit crab

64 Spider

65 The egg-case of a shark or skate

66 They are carried on the wind

67 Frogs or toads

68 In a herd

pages 38–39

69 Brush

70 Purplish-black

71 A botanist

72 A horse (a young female)

73 Blossom

74 The dove

75 Husky

76 Polar bear

77 Africa

78 In the daytime

79 Black rats

80 A crescent or U-shape

Answers

81 Its tail

pages 40-41

82 Giraffe

83 Coniferous

84 A horse

85 Dingo

86 Shellfish, especially clams and mussels

87 Genet (a mammal)

88 A snail

89 South America

90 Their mother's milk

91 Fish

92 Palm

93 Stag or buck

94 Desert

95 No

pages 42-43

96 Weeping willow

97 Koala

98 A lizard

99 Rolls into a ball

100 Three

101 In its mouth

102 Gorilla

103 Kangaroo

104 Monkeys

105 A pack

106 Insects

107 Bulls

108 Eight

109 Cuckoo

pages 44-45

110 Three

111 Flamingo

112 A pod

113 Australia

114 Bamboo

115 The whale shark

116 Camel

117 Arachnophobia

118 Africa

119 Ten

120 Crocodile

121 Platypus

122 Fish

123 Gills

Answers

124 F (It has one.)
125 F (It's an antelope.)
126 T
127 T
128 F
129 T
130 F (A manta ray is a fish.)
131 F
132 F (They are mammals.)
133 T
134 T
135 F (It is part of a mammal's ear.)
136 T
137 T

Answers

CHAPTER 3

pages 48–49
1 A red flag
2 By touching the wall
3 Jack
4 Japan
5 Seven
6 Tuba
7 Eagle

pages 50–51
8 Ian Thorpe
9 Brazil
10 Tee
11 Frames
12 Mountains
13 501
14 Boxing
15 1500m

pages 52–53
16 Swimming
17 Tutu
18 Nine

19 Can-can
20 Judo
21 Double six
22 1 mile
23 Croquet
24 Polo
25 Monopoly
26 Unicycle
27 Baton
28 Paper

pages 54–55
29 Fencing
30 Four
31 Russian
32 Zero
33 64
34 Third
35 Black
36 Five
37 Skis
38 Horse
39 3 minutes
40 Sand

Answers

41 Eleven

42 A combination of all four strokes

43 Five

44 Violin

45 When two batters are out in one go

46 Australia

47 Two

48 Mixed Martial Arts

49 Kick off

50 Rio de Janeiro, Brazil

51 Horse

52 Tennis

53 Bullseye

54 Every four years

55 Karaoke

56 Three

57 Knight

58 Tennis

59 Flute

60 Five

61 Four

62 It should take 4 shots to put the ball in the hole

63 Cue ball

64 Formula One

65 Seven

66 A hat trick

67 Spins on one leg

68 The boundary

69 An ace

70 Fishing

71 Wimbledon

72 Basketball

73 Three

74 Six

75 Ice hockey

76 Boxing

77 Netball

78 Oval

79 New Zealand

80 Grass

Answers

81 Ballet

82 Nine

83 Soccer

84 Six

85 Boxing

86 Hearts, diamonds, clubs, and spades

87 Four

88 Cricket

89 Italy

90 Curling

91 Soccer

pages 64–65

92 Three

93 Bagpipes

94 Knockout

95 Bends at the knees

96 Slippery track

97 Shake them

98 Baseball

99 Four

100 Soccer

101 Rugby

102 Four

103 Basketball

pages 66–67

104 Tennis

105 Dance

106 Goalkeeper

107 Baseball

108 American football

109 Ten

110 18

111 Cycling

112 Free throw line

113 Four

114 Basketball

115 Carries a player's clubs and gives advice

116 Two

117 When the snitch is caught

pages 68–69

118 F (It is square.)

119 F (Backstroke is done first.)

120 F (They are from Italy.)

121 T

Answers

122 T

123 T

124 T

125 F (It means "folding" and "paper".)

126 T

127 T

128 F (It is known as calcio in Italy.)

129 T

Answers

CHAPTER 4

1 Malaria
2 Fossils
3 Venus
4 Convex
5 Agoraphobia
6 Michael
7 Chimpanzee

8 Electric current
9 Lungs
10 Valentina Tereshkova
11 Peristalsis
12 Butterflies
13 Satellite
14 The spine
15 Isaac Newton

16 Artificial intelligence
17 Venus
18 24 (in 12 pairs)
19 Nausea or nauseous
20 Carbon
21 Pupil
22 Spiders
23 Filament
24 Canine
25 Diabetes
26 Water
27 The Moon
28 Smell

29 32
30 Bug and worm
31 The Milky Way
32 Blood
33 Birds
34 Heart
35 Albert
36 In the upper leg
37 Insects
38 The nucleus
39 Once
40 Extinction
41 Iron

Answers

pages 78–79

42 Carbon dioxide

43 Venus

44 Neon

45 Lightning

46 In your head (It's part of your brain.)

47 Saturn

48 Opaque

49 Security or antivirus

50 Gravity

51 Blood

52 Central processing unit

53 Body temperature

54 Contract

pages 80–81

55 Salt

56 Ribs

57 Herbivore

58 Oxygen

59 Plants

60 Mars

61 Nitrogen

62 Horse

63 Mercury, Venus, Earth, and Mars

64 Arm

65 Cosmonaut

66 Dirt and particles that could harm the eye

67 Isaac

pages 82–83

68 Jupiter

69 A vine

70 Electronic

71 Four

72 Thighs

73 Earth

74 Feline

75 Two

76 Green

77 Quads or quadruplets

78 9

79 The voice box

80 Einstein

81 Mercury

pages 84–85

82 Cattle or cow-like

Answers

83 The nose (in between the nostrils)

84 Optician

85 Ice (frozen water)

86 Apple Inc.

87 Laptop

88 Mars

89 Drone

90 Submarine

91 Headphones

92 Silk

93 File transfer protocol

94 Voyager

pages 86–87

95 Hydrogen

96 Read-only memory

97 The Moon

98 Heart

99 Microsoft

100 Splits

101 Jupiter, Saturn, Uranus, and Neptune

102 Spokes

103 Migration

104 Eight

105 Neptune

106 Bridge

107 Internet

pages 88–89

108 T

109 F (It carries a negative charge.)

110 F

111 T

112 F (The stomach is affected.)

113 T

114 T

115 F (They struggle with things close-up.)

116 T

117 T

118 F (It has no natural predators.)

119 T

Answers

CHAPTER 5

pages 90–91

1 Suspension
2 North America
3 Cook
4 12
5 Table Mountain
6 Nigeria
7 Natural gas

pages 92–93

8 Africa
9 1889
10 Earthquakes
11 Sweden
12 The capital
13 An eagle
14 Community
15 Aquifer

pages 94–95

16 Madrid
17 The Pacific Ocean
18 Blizzard
19 Canada

20 Europe
21 Compass
22 The Nile and Amazon
23 Earthquakes
24 North America
25 China
26 One World Trade Center
27 Africa
28 South Africa
29 Portugal

pages 96–97

30 Estuary
31 Washington, D.C.
32 Fossil fuels
33 Africa
34 Dune
35 The London Eye
36 Pisa
37 Los Angeles
38 Berlin
39 Russia
40 India
41 Canada
42 Hawaii

Answers

pages 98–99

43 Euro
44 Japan
45 The US
46 Gondola
47 National anthem
48 Six
49 Warrior
50 Chocolate
51 A thermometer
52 The Maori
53 St. Paul's
54 His head
55 Sailor
56 A hurricane

pages 100–101

57 The Nile
58 The rupee
59 Australia
60 New York
61 South America
62 Arctic
63 Italy
64 Holland
65 Igloo

66 New York
67 The Panama Canal
68 France
69 South America
70 Wellington (New Zealand)

pages 102–103

71 Stalactites and stalagmites
72 The Mediterranean
73 Lava
74 Atlantic and Pacific
75 Asia
76 Train
77 Fault
78 Japan
79 Clouds
80 New York
81 Italy
82 Weather
83 Ferry

pages 104–105

84 German
85 Africa

Answers

86 Metamorphic

87 Rome

88 Alaska

89 Switzerland

90 Forecasting

91 Greece

92 A lion

93 South America

94 Mount Etna

95 A wide-brimmed hat from Mexico

96 Australia

97 Peso

pages 106–107

98 Alaska

99 Avalanche

100 Plane

101 Gravy

102 New York

103 The Great Pyramids

104 Emperor

105 Fossil

106 Pancakes

107 Tokyo

108 Asia

109 Colorado River

pages 108–109

110 F (Two—Alaska and Hawaii)

111 F

112 T

113 T

114 T

115 F (It was given by France.)

116 T

117 F (Igneous rocks are formed this way.)

118 F (5 - Superior, Michigan, Huron, Ontario, Erie)

119 T

120 F (Stalactites hang from the ceiling, stalagmites grow from the floor.)

121 T